ABORIGINAL
MOSAICS
COLORING BOOK

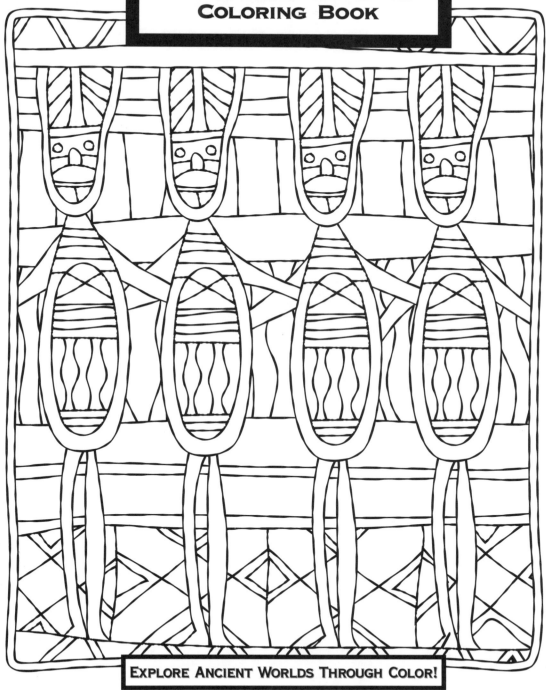

EXPLORE ANCIENT WORLDS THROUGH COLOR!

MindWare®
brainy toys for kids of all ages®

www.MINDWAREonline.com

A MindWare® Original!

Our entire selection of Brainy Toys for Kids of All Ages® is available at www.MINDWAREonline.com or by calling us at 800-999-0398 to request a catalog.

Coloring Books

Color your imagination wild! Each of our coloring books offer one of a kind patterns, textures and styles you make your own by choosing just how to bring them to life.

Animal Babies Coloring Book Series
Learn interesting facts as you color young animals in their habitats in *Rainforest & Tropical Babies, Desert & Savanna Babies, Forest & Grassland Babies* and *Ocean & Wetland Babies.*

Creature Camouflage Coloring Book Series
Conceal or uncover captivating creatures in *Hidden Exoskeletons, Hidden Feathers, Hidden Scales* and *Shells and Hidden Fur.*

Designs Coloring Book Series
From tessellating art to optical illusions, let your inner artist emerge in *PrismDesigns, UltraDesigns, GeoDesigns* and *OptiDesigns.*

Scapes Coloring Book Series
Explore the styles of great artists, nature's symmetry, abstract patterns and architectural details in *MasterScapes, EnviroScapes, DesignScapes* and *ArchiScapes.*

Quilts Coloring Book Series
Try your hand at creating stunning patterns without ever threading a needle in *Modern Threads, Common Threads, Threads of Time* and *Threads of Tradition.*

Mosaics Coloring Book Series
Unearth the beauty of one of history's oldest and most enduring art forms in *Classic Mosaics, Aboriginal Mosaics, Celtic Mosaics* and *Aztec Mosaics.*

Lights Coloring Book Series
These unique stained glass coloring books are printed on special vellum-like paper. Watch the light burst through each dazzling color in *EuroLights, SpinLights, TesseLights* and *EcoLights.*

Puzzle Books

Our puzzle books build skills in many areas—from logic to math, spatial reasoning to verbal skills.

Deducibles
Strengthen deduction and logic skills by using clues to eliminate and sequence puzzle letters revealing the solution. Teaches direction following and methodical thinking.

Analogy Challenges
Verbal challenges in a puzzle format promote the skills needed to be a logical thinker. Learn to analyze analogies by relationship, category and structure.

Noodlers
Solve these highly graphic, spatial reasoning puzzles by using the provided "noodle" sticks. These puzzles are harder than they appear, and very addictive.

Word Winks
Verbal visual puzzles help develop both creative and analytical skills. Phrases and idioms are represented by illustrated symbols and words.

Perplexors
This innovative logic series sharpens deductive reasoning skills with a simple "cross out and circle" technique and entertaining stories.

Venn Perplexors
Students define relationships and characteristics. Strengthens logic and problem solving skills with fun stories and pictures to catch and keep their attention.

Grid Perplexors
Through the process of elimination, plus handy pre-printed grids for organizing deductions, students will build their ability to think through complex problems and integrate logic into other disciplines.

Logic Links
Logic puzzle books that build spatial skills through manipulative play. Pop out the brightly colored chips from the back cover, read the clues and let the logic loose!

Math Path Puzzles
These unique math books teach students to visualize the relationships between numbers—boosting math confidence.

Addition Adventures and Subtraction Secrets
Students solve addition and subtraction problems and use the answers to plot their way. At the end of the path is a pot of gold, a secret message or a missing pet lizard.

Multiplication Mosaics and Division Designs
Mosaics and designs are created when students solve multiplication and division problems and put their answers onto a grid, revealing dazzling patterns and pictures.

Tan-Tastic Tangrams
A starter tangram book for students who are ramping up to geometric visual challenges. Comes with pop-out tangram pieces.

ISBN 1-892069-35-0

for other MindWare products visit our website
www.MINDWAREonline.com

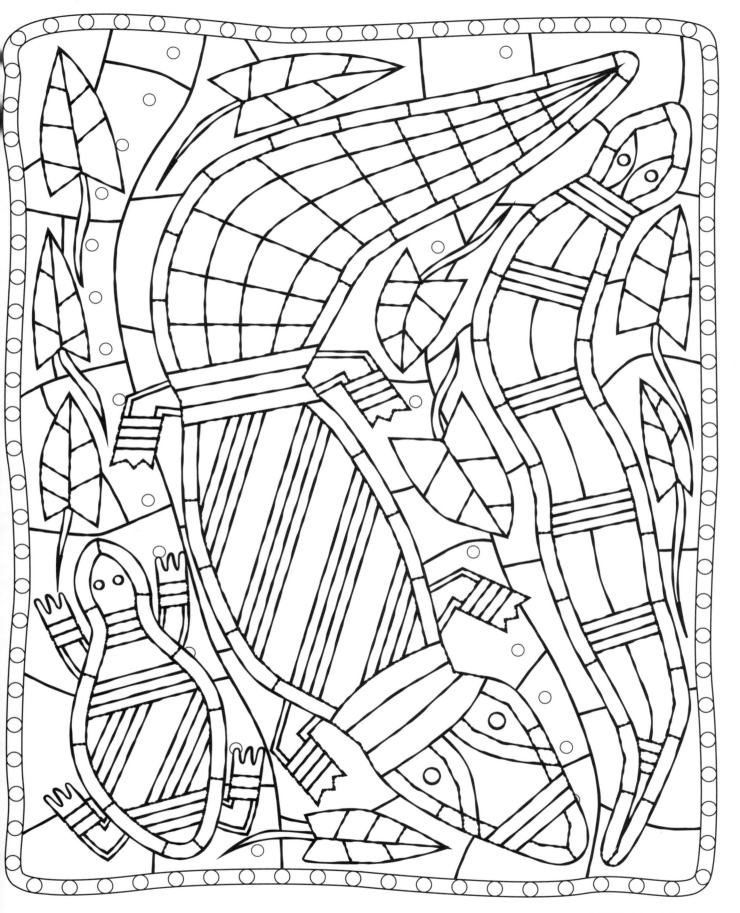

LOOK

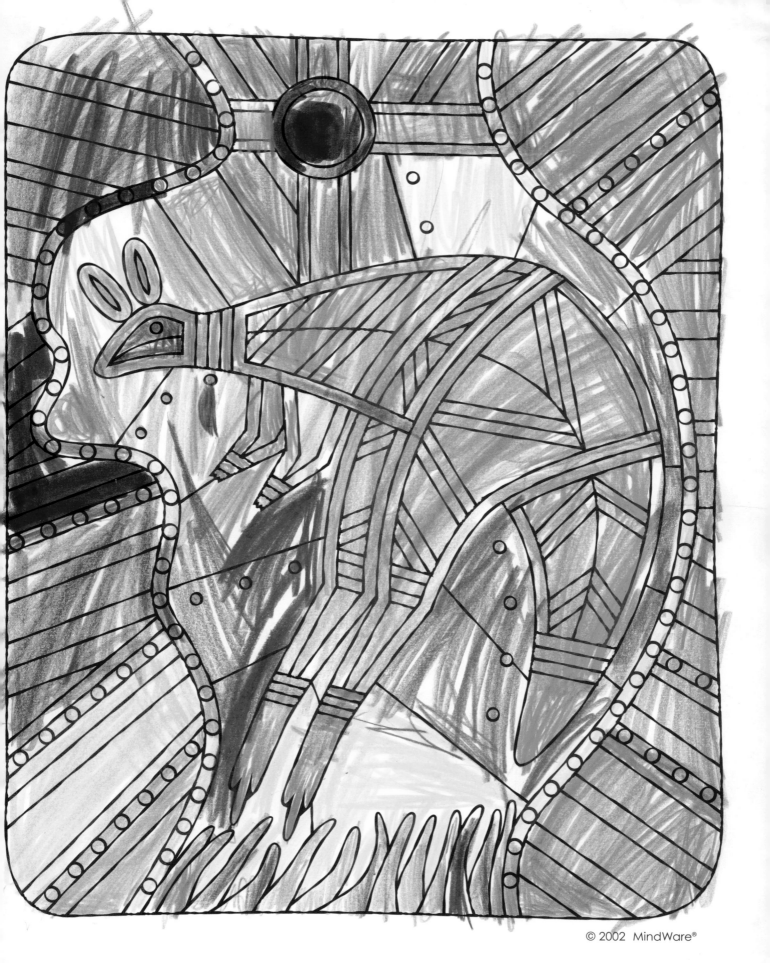

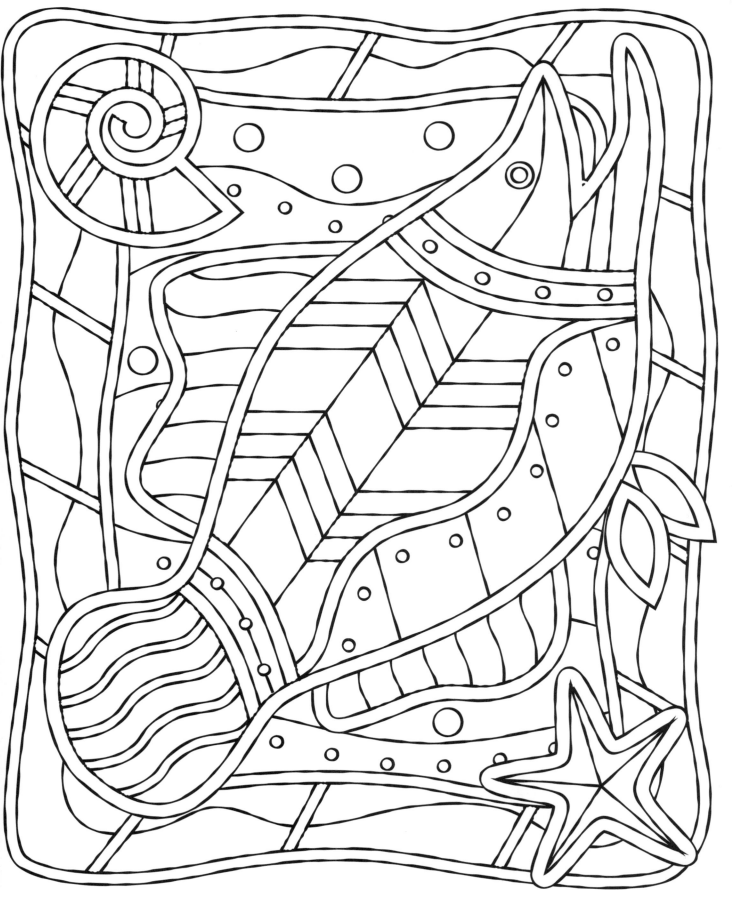

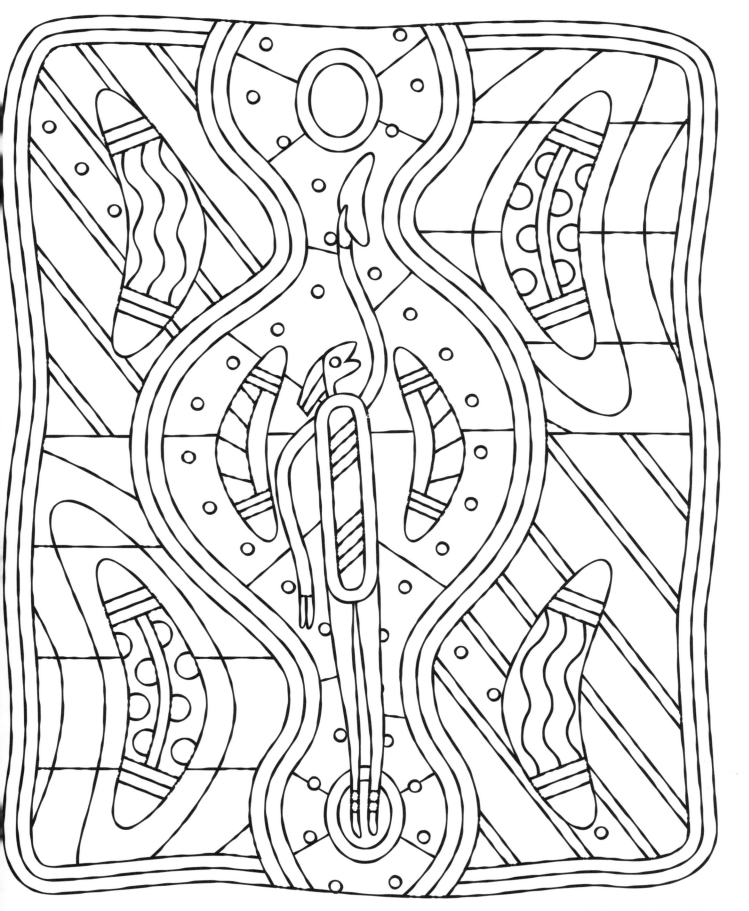

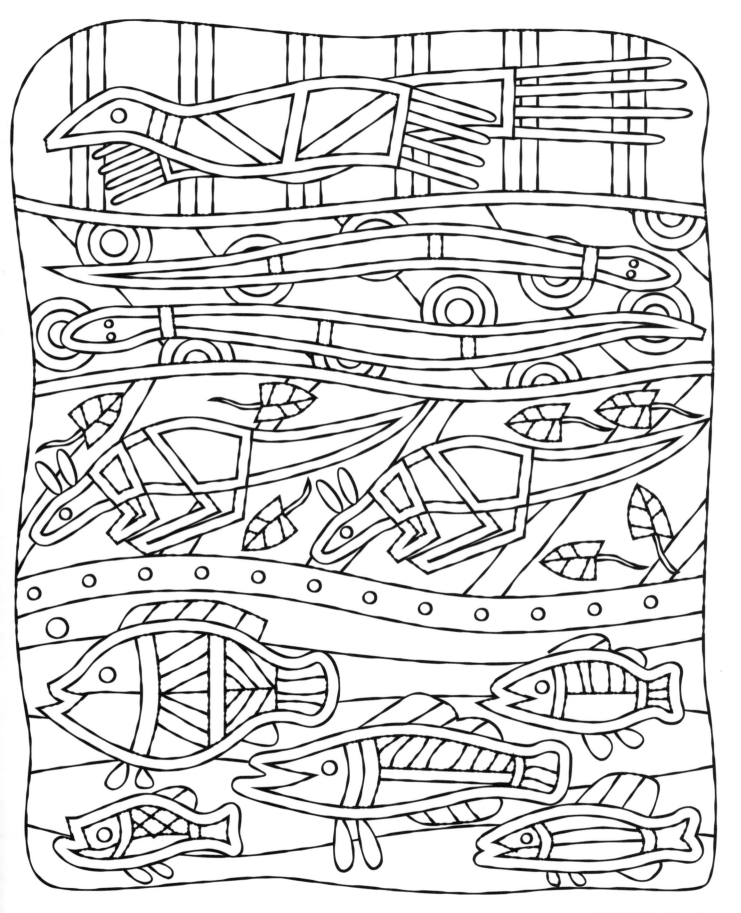

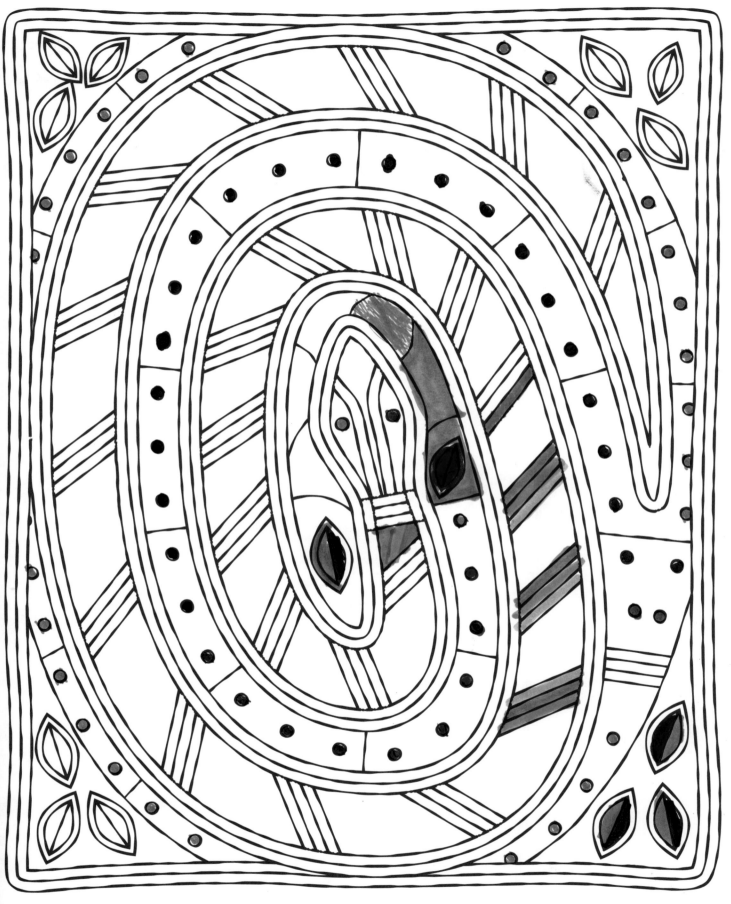

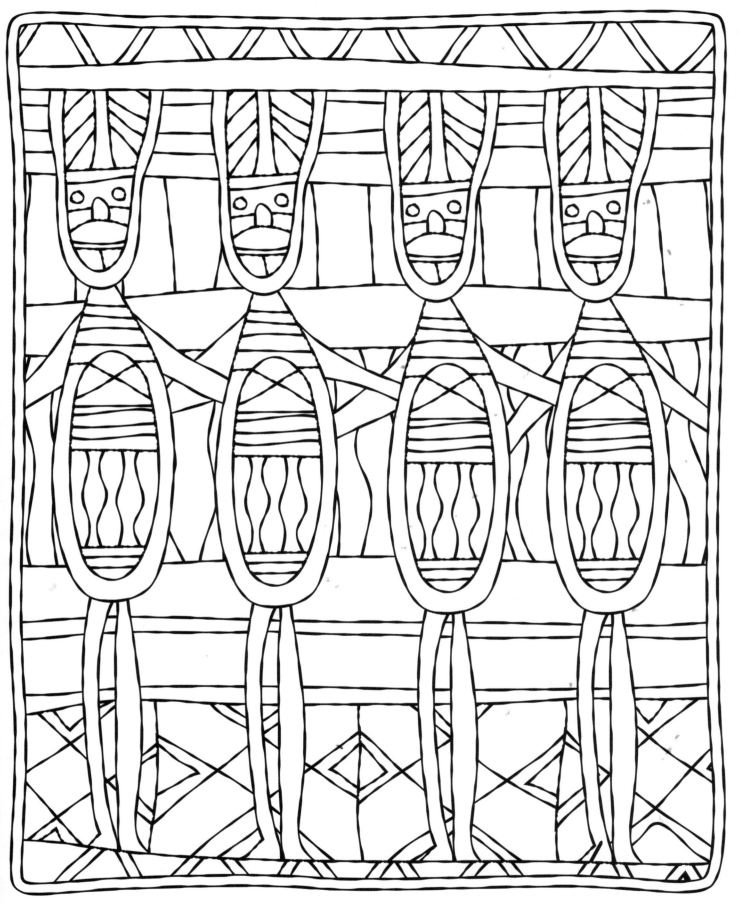

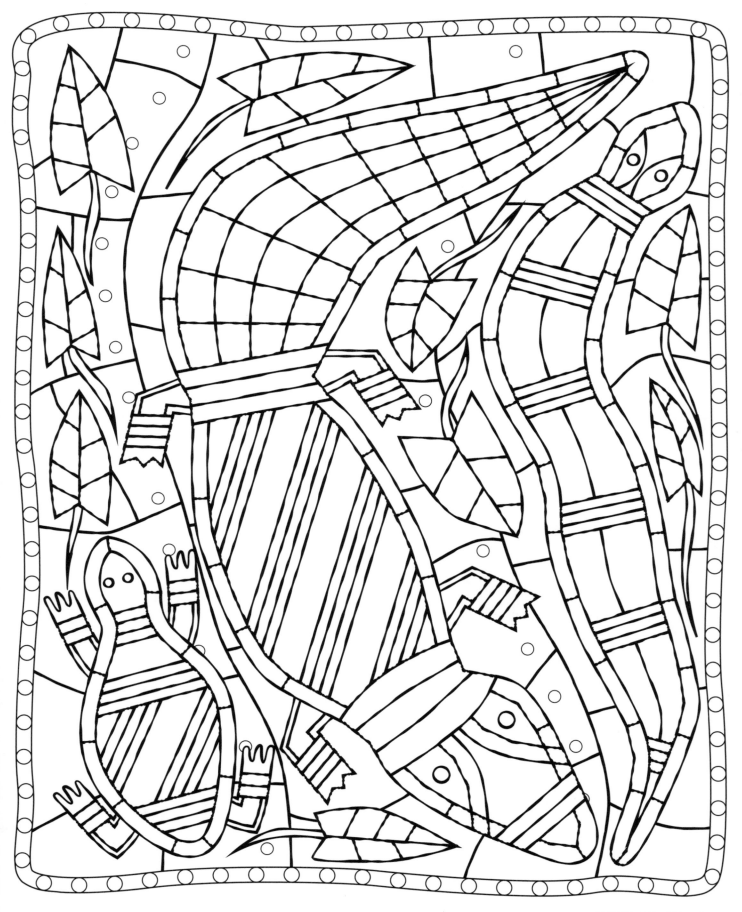

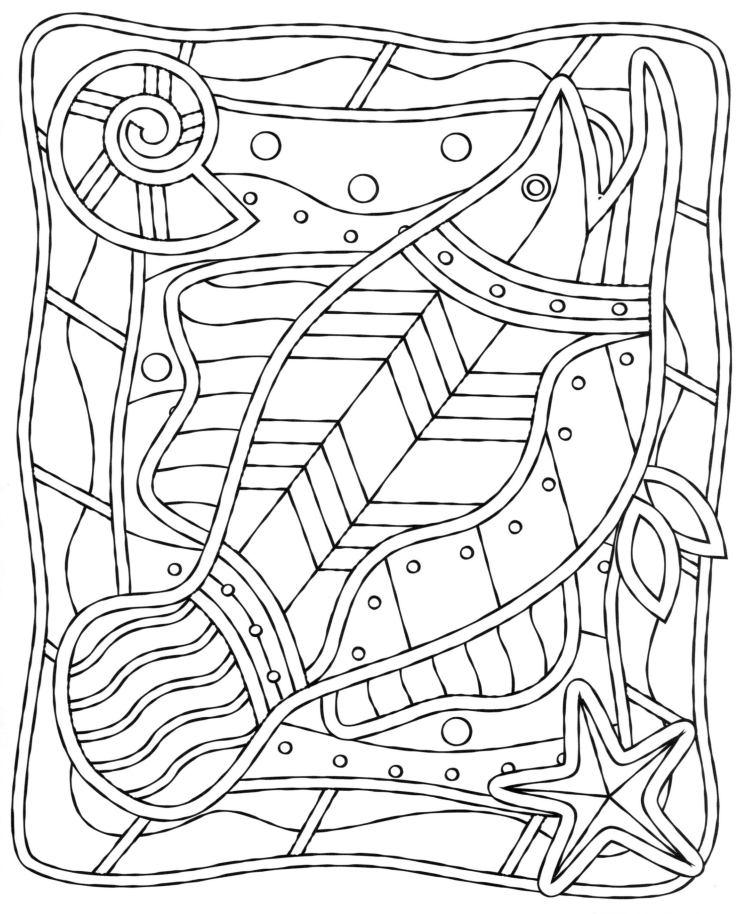

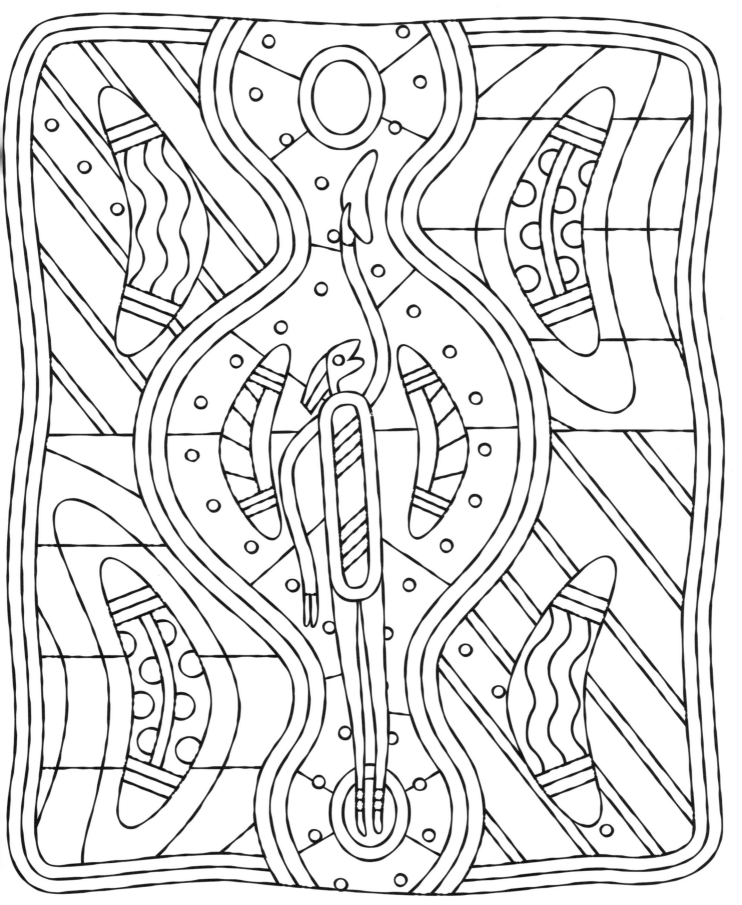

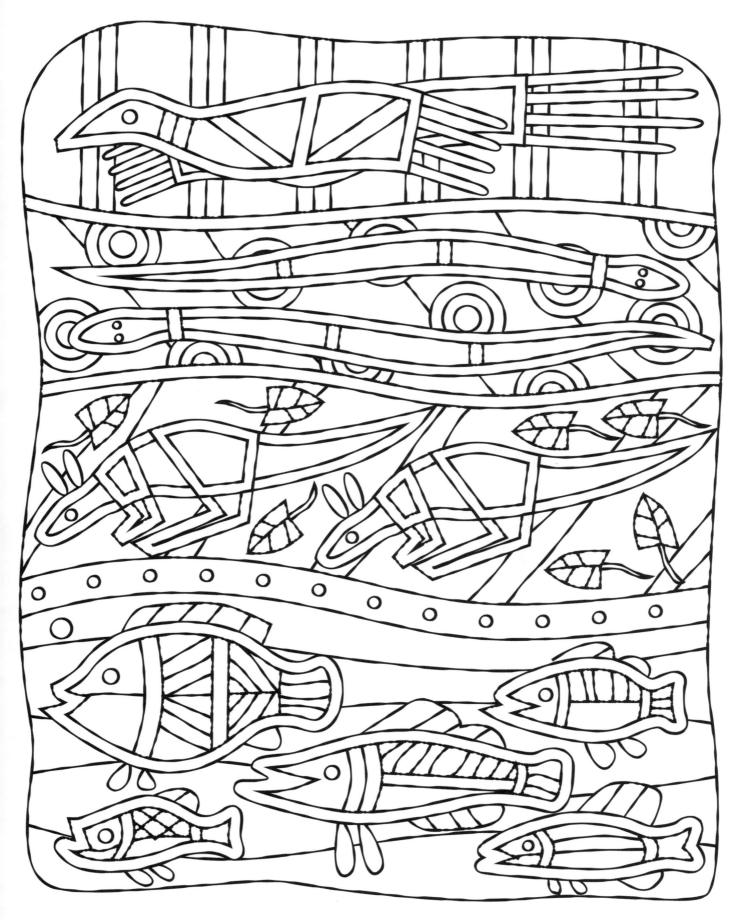

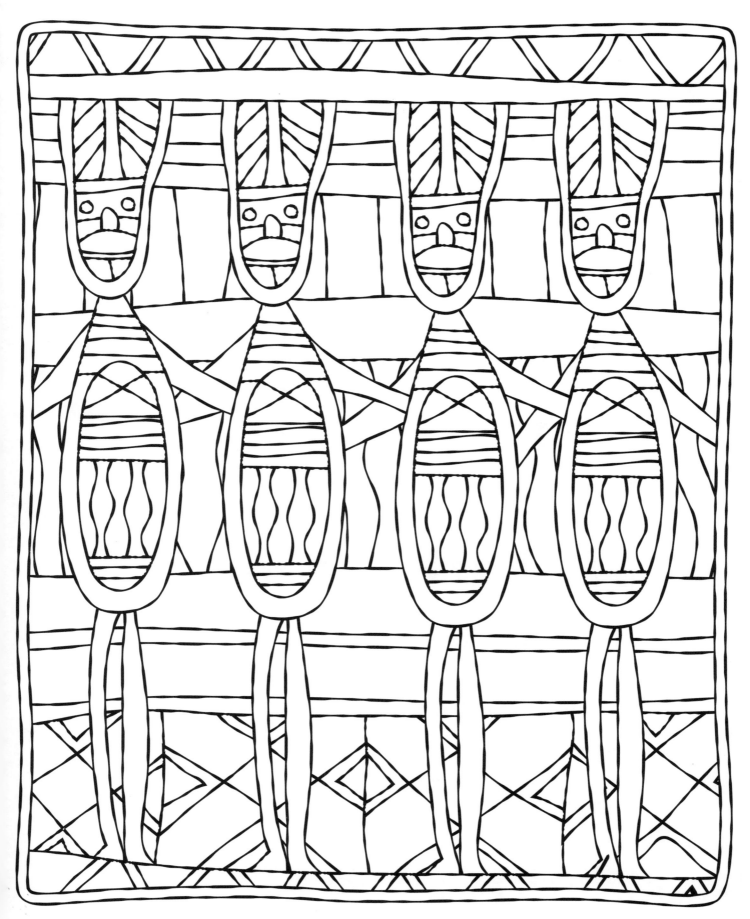